Poetry and Verse for Urban Children

BOOK I

Poems And Verses To Begin On

POEMS
AND VERSES
TO BEGIN
ON

*

Donald J. Bissett, Editor

CHANDLER PUBLISHING COMPANY
124 Spear Street
San Francisco California 94105

4

INTRODUCTION

Poetry is often best understood and most fully enjoyed when read aloud. Perhaps this is a major reason why poetry seems to have special appeal to young children —it is read aloud to them.

Young children's enthusiasm for poetry is fortunate as poetry can contribute much to children's language development. The essential elements of poetry, its form, rhythm, words, and subject matter, make it a rich resource for language learning. The teacher knows intuitively the special place poetry has in children's language development.

This collection of poems is intended for teachers who know the satisfaction of reading aloud for young children, but who may often have wished for poetry books of more manageable size than the usual thick-as-a-brick anthology. This book is the first of a series of useful, entertaining anthologies, clearly organized and indexed for teacher convenience, yet small enough to be slipped into pocket or purse for easy portability.

The poems and verses in *Poems And Verses To Begin On* have been chosen for urban children of nursery-school, kindergarten, and first-grade age. The subject matter of the poems follows that of the CHANDLER READING PROGRAM; but these poems and verses will appeal to city children in any reading or reading-readiness program.

The poems and verses have been arranged in four categories:

Rhymes about Childhood Experience
Rhymes about City Experience
Rhymes and Rhythms
Rhymes from Mother Goose

Teachers interested in techniques of reading aloud will find a section titled "Hints for Reading Poetry Aloud" following the poems and verses, as well as suggestions for using certain selections in the book. A bibliography of poetry books recommended for use with young children is also included for those teachers interested in finding additional good poems and verses.

I am indebted to the librarians in the Frederic Burk School Library, San Francisco, California, in the Childrens Room at the Main Branch of the Public Library in Syracuse, New York, and in the Childrens Room, Fifth Avenue Branch of the New York City Public Library, who assisted in providing material from which the poems in this collection were chosen. I am indebted also to Andy Nicholaw, who patiently and efficiently typed the manuscript, and to the editorial staff at Chandler Publishing Company for their support and assistance.

To the many school children—in San Francisco, Cleveland, New York City, New Haven—who have listened to the poems in the collection, this book is affectionately dedicated. Their reactions influenced the final selection for *Poems And Verses to Begin On*.

DONALD J. BISSETT

CONTENTS

✳ RHYMES ABOUT CITY EXPERIENCE

∽ RHYMES AND RHYTHMS

☞ RHYMES FROM MOTHER GOOSE

Rhymes about Childhood Experience

*Some experiences are common to all
children, no matter where they live—in
the heart of the city, in the suburbs, or
in rural areas. Although some adults
fail to realize the significance of experiences basic to childhood, poets do not.*

*The poetry in this section inter-
prets experiences common to childhood.
These poems and verses can be read to
children once, or read and re-read many
times. Most of the verses are easy for
the teacher to memorize; the children
will delight in memorizing many.*

SATURDAY MORNING

Myra Cohn Livingston

Please let's stop
At the barbershop
And cut my hair
For a lollipop.

IT TICKLES

Myra Cohn Livingston

It tickles
    when I brush
    my teeth.
Not on top,
But underneath.

MY MOTHER SAID

Arnold Spilka

My mother said,
"Don't jump in bed!"
And so I don't,
I hop instead.

REFLECTION

Myra Cohn Livingston

In the mirror
I can see
Lots of things
But mostly—me.

EVERYBODY SAYS

Dorothy Aldis

Everybody says
I look just like my mother.
Everybody says
I'm the image of Aunt Bee.
Everybody says
My nose is like my father's
But *I* want to look like ME!

MY NAME

Myra Cohn Livingston

My name is most especially
The thing they use for calling me.

CATHERINE

Karla Kuskin

Catherine said "I think I'll bake
A most delicious chocolate cake."
She took some mud and mixed it up
While adding water from a cup
And then some weeds and nuts and bark
And special gravel from the park
A thistle and a dash of sand.
She beat out all the lumps by hand.
And on the top she wrote "To You"
The way she says the bakers do
And then she signed it "Fondly C."
And gave the whole of it to me.
I thanked her but I wouldn't dream
Of eating cake without ice cream.

FEET

Dorothy Aldis

There are things
Feet know
That hands never will:
The exciting
Pounding feel
Of running down a hill;

The soft cool
Prickliness
When feet are bare
Walking in
The summer grass
To almost anywhere;

Or dabbling in
Water all
Slip-Sliddering through toes—
(Nicer than
Through fingers though why
No one really knows.)

"Toes, tell my
Fingers," I
Said to them one day,
"Why it's such
Fun just to
Wiggle and play."

But toes just
Looked at me
Solemn and still.
Oh, there are things
Feet know
That hands NEVER WILL.

WALKING

Grace Ellen Glaubitz

When Daddy
Walks
With Jean and me,
We have a
Lot of fun
'Cause we can't
Walk as fast
As he,
Unless we
Skip and
Run!
I stretch,
And stretch
My legs so far,
I nearly slip
And fall—
But how
Does Daddy
Take such steps?
He doesn't stretch
At all!

HANDS

Dorothy Aldis

There are things
Hands do
That feet never can. Oh
Lots of things
Like stringing beads
Or playing the piano;

Or plaiting little
Stems of grass
Into a little braid
For an acorn
Dolly's head
That somebody has made.

Or shelling slippery
Pods of peas
So the peas can pop;
Or holding things
Quite tightly so
They will not slip or drop.

"Hands, tell my
Toes," I
Said to them one day,
"How you learned
To do so much
More useful things than they."

But hands just
Looked at me
And proudly began:
"Oh, there are things
Hands do
That feet NEVER CAN."

BUMP ON MY KNEE

Myra Cohn Livingston

Look at the terrible bump
    on my knee
(I thought I was playing carefully,
    but the wheel turned round
    and I suddenly found
    myself on the ground)
It doesn't hurt terribly
    but I think
    I would like
    you to paint it
    a
    beautiful
    pink!

NAUGHTY SOAP SONG

Dorothy Aldis

Just when I'm ready to
Start on my ears,
That is the time that my
Soap disappears.

It jumps from my fingers and
Slithers and slides
Down to the end of the
Tub, where it hides.

And acts in a most diso-
Bedient way
AND THAT'S WHY MY SOAP'S
    GROWING
THINNER EACH DAY.

AN INDIGNANT MALE

A. B. Ross

The way they scrub
Me in the tub,
I think there's
Hardly
Any
Doubt
Sometime they'll rub,
And rub and rub
Until they simply
Rub
Me
Out.

SEE, I CAN DO IT

Dorothy Aldis

See, I can do it all myself
With my own little brush!
The tooth paste foams inside my mouth.
The faucet waters rush.

In and out and underneath
And round and round and round:
First I do my upstairs teeth
And then I do my down—

The part I like the best of it
Is at the end, though, when I spit.

AFTER A BATH

Aileen Fisher

After my bath
I try, try, try
to wipe myself
till I'm dry, dry, dry.

Hands to wipe
and fingers and toes
and two wet legs
and a shiny nose.

Just think how much
less time I'd take
if I were a dog
and could shake, shake, shake.

BED IN SUMMER

Robert Louis Stevenson

In winter I get up at night
And dress by yellow candle-light.
In summer, quite the other way,
I have to go to bed by day.

I have to go to bed and see
The birds still hopping on the tree,
Or hear the grown-up people's feet
Still going past me in the street.

And does it not seem hard to you,
When all the sky is clear and blue,
And I should like so much to play,
To have to go to bed by day?

HAPPY THOUGHT

Robert Louis Stevenson

The world is so full
    of a number of things.
I'm sure we should all
    be as happy as kings.

GOING TO BED

Marchette Chute

I'm always told to hurry up—
  Which I'd be glad to do,
If there were not so many things
  That need attending to.

But first I have to find my towel
  Which fell behind the rack,
And when a pillow's thrown at me
  I have to throw it back.

And then I have to get the things
  I need in bed with me.
Like marbles and my birthday train
  And Pete the chimpanzee.

I have to see my polliwog
  Is safely in its pan,
And stand a minute on my head
  To be quite sure I can.

I have to bounce upon my bed
  To see if it will sink,
And then when I am covered up
  I find I need a drink.

GOING TO SLEEP

Dorothy Aldis

The safest feeling
In the world
Is to be lying
Warm and curled
In bed while in
The room next door
They talk; and then
Don't any more. . . .

WIDE AWAKE

Myra Cohn Livingston

I have to jump up
    out of bed
    and stretch my hands
    and rub my head,
    and curl my toes
    and yawn
    and shake
    myself
    all wide-awake!

I WOKE UP THIS MORNING

Karla Kuskin

I woke up this morning
At quarter past seven.
I kicked up the covers
And stuck out my toe.
And ever since then
(That's a quarter past seven)
They haven't said anything
Other than "No."
They haven't said anything
Other than "Please, dear,
Don't do what you're doing,"
Or "Lower your voice."
Whatever I've done
And however I've chosen,
I've done the wrong thing
And I've made the wrong choice.
I didn't wash well
And I didn't say thank you.
I didn't shake hands
And I didn't say please.
I didn't say sorry.
When passing the candy
I banged the box into
Miss Witelson's knees.
I didn't say sorry.
I didn't stand straighter.
I didn't speak louder
When asked what I'd said.

Well, I said
That tomorrow
At quarter past seven
They can
Come in and get me.
I'm Staying In Bed.

TOASTER TIME

Eve Merriam

Tick tick tick tick tick tick tick
Toast up a sandwich quick quick quick
Hamwich
Jamwich
Lick lick lick!

Tick tick tick tick tick tick—stop!
POP!

A MATTER OF TASTE

Eve Merriam

What does your tongue like the most?
Chewy meat or crunchy toast?

A lumpy bumpy pickle or tickly pop?
A soft marshmallow or a hard lime drop?

Hot pancakes or a sherbet freeze?
Celery noise or quiet cheese?
Or do you like pizza
More than any of these?

HOT CHOCOLATE

Dorothy Aldis

I climb the tallest drugstore stool
And order a Hot Chocolate.
"Coffee please," my mother says.
Now we have to sit and wait.

My chocolate comes with cream on top.
I feel it steaming through the cup—
Too hot to taste, but I don't care:
I can twirl here on this stool
Until my chocolate does get cool
And then I'll drink it up.

JAM

Russell Hoban

Jam in the morning, jam at noon,
Bread and jam by the light of the moon.
 Jam
 is
 very
 nice.
Jam on biscuits, jam on toast,
Jam is the thing that I like most.
Jam is sticky, jam is sweet,
Jam is tasty, jam's a treat—
 Raspberry
 Strawberry
 Gooseberry,
I'm very
FOND OF JAM!

ANIMAL CRACKERS

Christopher Morley

Animal crackers, and cocoa to drink,
That is the finest of suppers, I think;
When I'm grown up and can have what I
    please
I think I shall always insist upon these.

What do *you* choose when you're offered a treat?
When Mother says, "What would you like best
    to eat?"
Is it waffles and syrup, or cinnamon toast?
It's cocoa and animals that *I* love the most!

The kitchen's the cosiest place that I know:
The kettle is singing, the stove is aglow,
And there in the twilight, how jolly to see
The cocoa and animals waiting for me.

Daddy and Mother dine later in state,
With Mary to cook for them, Susan to wait;
But they don't have nearly as much fun as I
Who eat in the kitchen with Nurse standing by;
And Daddy once said, he would like to be me
Having cocoa and animals once more for tea!

SONG FOR SUPPER

J. Lilian Vandervere

Baked potato, crackly brown,
Melted butter running down.
    But applesauce for supper
    Is what I like instead:
    Applesauce for supper
    And a slice of raisin bread.

Eggs all scrambled, piping hot,
Served with bacon, like as not.
    But applesauce for supper
    Is what I like the most:
    Applesauce for supper
    And a piece of crunchy toast.

Sometimes cocoa, hot and sweet,
Pudding for a special treat.
    But applesauce for supper
    Is what I like, don't you?
    Applesauce for supper
    And a ginger cookie, too.

LITTLE SOUNDS

Beatrice Schenk de Regniers

Underneath the big sounds
underneath the big silences
Listen for the little secret sounds.

Listen.
ts ts
That is the little sound of the sugar,
the little loaf of sugar
deep inside the cup of hot black coffee.
ts ts
That is what the sugar says.

Listen for the little secret sounds.
Sh! be very quiet and listen.
tck tck tck tck tck tck tck tck
That is the little sound of your father's watch.
tck tck tck tck tck tck tck tck
It makes such a tiny hurrying scurrying sound.

Listen for the little sounds always.
When a pussycat licks her fur
can you hear a little sound?
When someone is licking an ice-cream cone
can you hear?

Did you ever hear
a rabbit biting a lettuce leaf?
a cow switching her tail?
a tiny baby breathing?

Listen
to the little sound of
a letter dropping into a letter box,
a pin falling to the floor,
a leaf falling from a tree,
dry leaves crunching under your feet.

Listen to the little secret sound
of a pencil writing on paper,
of a scissors snipping your fingernails,
of a flower stem breaking when you pick a
    flower.

Listen for the little sounds always—
Listen.

KEEP A POEM IN YOUR POCKET

Beatrice Schenk de Regniers

Keep a poem in your pocket
and a picture in your head
and you'll never feel lonely
at night when you're in bed.

The little poem will sing to you
the little picture bring to you
a dozen dreams to dance to you
at night when you're in bed.

So—
Keep a picture in your pocket
and a poem in your head
and you'll never feel lonely
at night when you're in bed.

Rhymes
about
City
Experiences

Much poetry has been written about the countryside and its quiet pastoral scene; less has been written about the environment of the city. But the sounds and sights of the city do lend themselves to poetic expression. The poems in this section interpret city living— rain in the city, city traffic and buildings, the city park and its trees, swings, slides, and drinking fountains, and other aspects of city living that urban children know.

"SH"

James S. Tippett

"Sh!" says mother,
"Sh!" says father.
"Running in the hall
Is a very great bother."

"Mrs. Grumpy Grundy,
Who lives down below,
Will come right up
First thing you know."

"Sh!" says father,
"Sh!" says mother.
"Can't you play a quiet game
Of some kind or other?"

THE FROST PANE

David McCord

What's the good of breathing
On the window
Pane
In summer?
You can't write a
Nalphabet,
You can't draw a
Nelephant;
You can't make a smudge
With your nose
In summer.

Lots of good, breathing
On the window
Pane
In winter.
You can make a frost
On the window pane
In winter.
A white frost, a light frost,
A thick frost, a quick frost,
A write-me-out-a-picture frost
Across the pane
In winter.

NO DRIP OF RAIN

Ivy O. Eastwick

It rained on Anne,
it rained on Fan,
it rained on Arabella,
but—
it did not rain
on Mary Jane—
SHE had a HUGE umbrella.

RAIN

Myra Cohn Livingston

Summer rain
   is soft and cool,
   so I go barefoot
   in a pool.
But winter rain
   is cold, and pours,
   so I must watch it
   from indoors.

IT IS RAINING

Lucy Sprague Mitchell

It is raining.

Where would you like to be in the rain?
Where would you like to be?

I'd like to be on a city street,
where the rain comes down in a driving sheet,
where it wets the houses—roof and wall—
the wagons and horses and autos and all.
That's where I'd like to be in the rain,
that's where I'd like to be.

It is raining.

Where would you like to be in the rain?
Where would you like to be?

I'd like to be in a tall tree top,
where the rain comes dripping, drop, drop, drop,
around on every side:
where it wets the farmer, the barn, the pig,
the cows, the chickens both little and big;
where it batters and beats on a field of wheat
and makes the little birds hide.

It is raining.

Where would you like to be in the rain?
Where would you like to be?

I'd like to be on a ship at sea,
where everything's wet as wet can be
and the waves are rolling high,
where sailors are pulling the ropes and
     singing,
and wind's in the rigging and salt spray's
     stinging,
and round us sea gulls cry.
On a dipping skimming ship at sea—
that's where I'd like to be in the rain;
that's where I'd like to be!

RAIN

Robert Louis Stevenson

The rain is raining all around,
   It falls on field and tree,
It rains on the umbrellas here,
   And on the ships at sea.

THE PARK

James S. Tippett

I'm glad that I
   Live near a park

For in the winter
   After dark

The park lights shine
   As bright and still

As dandelions
   On a hill.

DRINKING FOUNTAIN

Marchette Chute

When I climb up,
   to get a drink,
It doesn't work
   The way you'd think.

I turn it up.
   The water goes
And hits me right
   Upon the nose.

I turn it down
   To make it small
And don't get any
   Drink at all.

EMPTY LOT

Myra Cohn Livingston

I wonder who it was
   forgot
   to build
   and left the empty lot.

I wonder who it was
   and why
   they left
   the weeds and grasses high.

I guess they know
   that I would need
   a place to find
   a featherweed.

THE SWING

Robert Louis Stevenson

How do you like to go up in a swing,
    Up in the air so blue?
Oh, I do think it is the pleasantest thing
    Ever a child can do!

Up in the air and over the wall,
    Till I can see so wide,
Rivers and trees and cattle and all
    Over the countryside—

Till I look down on the garden green,
    Down on the roof so brown—
Up in the air I go flying again,
    Up in the air and down!

HELLO AND GOODBY

Mary Ann Hoberman

Hello and good-by
Hello and good-by

When I'm in a swing
Swinging low and then high,
Goodby to the ground
Hello to the sky.

Hello to the rain
Good-by to the sun,
Then hello again sun
When the rain is all done.

In blows the winter,
Away the birds fly.
Good-by and hello
Hello and good-by.

MY SILLY SHADOW

When I swing
I can see
My silly shadow
Follow me.

It changes shapes
And sizes, too.
It's a jumping frog
Or a kangaroo.

It bounces around.
It does a jig.
It sometimes looks
Like a dancing pig.

It won't stand still.
It climbs a tree.
It loops the loop
Like a bumble bee.

My silly shadow
Doesn't know
I'm the one
That makes him go!

TEETER-TOTTER

A. Nicholaw

I'll sit first on the teeter-totter
And push my weight down low.
You get on right after me
By standing on tip-toe.
Push your feet into the dirt—
Lift yourself up high!
Down we'll come and up we'll go,
Right up to the sky.

SLIDING

Marchette Chute

Down the slide
We ride, we ride.
Round we run, and then
Up we pop
To reach the top,
Down we come again.

SLIDING

Myra Cohn Livingston

We can slide
  down the hill
  or down the stair
  or down the street
or anywhere.

Or down the roof
  where the shingles broke,
Or down the trunk
  of the back-yard oak.

Down the slide
  or the ice
  or the slippery street,

We can slide
  on our sled
  or our skates
  or our feet.

Oh, it's lots of fun to go outside
And slide and slide and slide and slide.

HIDING

Mary Ann Hoberman

Where is Jonathan?
Where is Paul?
I can't find either of them at all.
I've looked and looked and looked so hard
Inside the house,
Around the yard,
But I can't find them anywhere.

They're hiding.

Where is Jonathan?
Where is Paul?
They do not answer when I call.
There's not a sound; there's not a squeak;
I wish that one of them would speak.

They're hiding.

Where is Jonathan?
Where is Paul?
I think I'll look behind that wall,
And if they're there, then they'll come out;
But if they're not, I'll stay and shout

I'm hiding!

EVERY TIME I CLIMB A TREE

David McCord

Every time I climb a tree
Every time I climb a tree
Every time I climb a tree
I scrape a leg
Or skin a knee
And every time I climb a tree
I find some ants
Or dodge a bee
And get the ants
All over me

And every time I climb a tree
Where have you been?
They say to me
But don't they know that I am free
Every time I climb a tree?
I like it best
To spot a nest
That has an egg
Or maybe three

And then I skin
The other leg
But every time I climb a tree
I see a lot of things to see
Swallows rooftops and TV

And all the fields and farms there be
Every time I climb a tree
Though climbing may be good for ants
It isn't awfully good for pants
But still it's pretty good for me
Every time I climb a tree

THE SECRET PLACE

Dorothy Aldis

Halfway up a certain tree
There's a place belongs to me.
Two branches make a little chair
And I like it sitting there.

I like it.
And it's secret too.
No grown-up guesses where I go.
And if he should, and climbed to it—
He would not fit, he would not fit!

THE GOLD-TINTED DRAGON

Karla Kuskin

What's the good of a wagon
Without any dragon
To pull you for mile after mile?
An elegant lean one
A gold-tinted green one
Wearing a dragonly smile.
You'll sweep down the valleys
You'll sail up the hills
Your dragon will shine in the sun
And as you rush by
The people will cry
"I wish that my wagon had one!"

KITE DAYS

Mark Sawyer

A kite, a sky, and a good firm breeze,
And acres of ground away from trees,
And one hundred yards of clean, strong string—
Oh boy, Oh boy! I call that spring!

MY KITE

Myra Cohn Livingston

It was splendid,
My kite—
It flew and it flew
When we let out the string
In the wind,
And we knew
   It would fly with the birds—
   It would fly to the sea—
Then its tail
Tangled up in a
Terrible tree.

P'S THE PROUD POLICEMAN

Phyllis McGinley

P's the proud Policeman
   With buttons polished neat.
He's pleased to put his hand up
   When you want to cross the street.
By daylight he protects you;
   He protects you through the dark,
And he points the way politely
   To the playground or the park.

STOP AND GO

Marie Louise Allen

The traffic lights we see ahead
Are sometimes green and sometimes red.
Red on top, and green below;
The red means STOP, the green means GO!

Green below—GO—GO—GO!
Red on top—STOP—STOP—STOP!

STOP—GO

Dorothy Baruch

Automobiles
In a row
Wait to go
While the signal says:
     STOP

Bells ring
Tingaling
Red light's gone!
Green light's on!
Horns blow!
And the row
Starts to
     GO

TRAFFIC LIGHT

Nona Keen Duffy

We're waiting, and we're waiting,
    And we're looking overhead;
For the signal light is orange.
    Now we see that it is red!

We're watching, and we're watching,
    And we're patient in between
While we're waiting for the changing
    Of the light from red to green.

We're waiting, and we're staying
    In the place right where we are;
But now the green is showing,
    And my mother starts the car!

BUILDINGS

Myra Cohn Livingston

Buildings are a great surprise,
Every one's a different size.

Offices
grow
long
and
high,
tall
enough
to
touch
the
sky.

Houses seem
more like a box,
made of glue
and building blocks.

Every time you look, you see
Buildings shaped quite differently.

Rhymes
and
Rhythms

*Children enjoy some poems and verses
primarily for their rhythm or rhyme.
Such verses need not be logical in the
usual sense, or necessarily understood
line by line, word by word. Their sometimes predictable, sometimes unpre-
dictable, use of sound and rhythm makes
them a joy to hear and chant.*

HAVING

William Jay Smith

A castle has
    a castle moat,
A river has
    a river boat,
An organ has
    an organ note,
A mountain has
    a mountain goat,
But look at my
    new overcoat!

BOO HOO

Arnold Spilka

Mable cried as she stood by the window,
Mable cried as she stood by the door.
Mable cried and her tears filled three buckets;
Mable cried as she sat on the floor.

Mable cried for oh so many hours,
Mable cried for oh so many more.
With her tears then she watered her flowers;
With the rest then she mopped up the floor.

OPPOSITES

Mary Ann Hoberman

The opposite of dark is light
The opposite of black is white
The opposite of dull is bright
   And I eat chocolate cake at night.

The opposite of loose is tight
The opposite of peace is fight
The opposite of wrong is right
   A circus is a silly sight.

The opposite of big is small
The opposite of short is tall
The opposite of none is all
   Now watch me bounce my rubber ball.

JUMP OR JIGGLE

Evelyn Beyer

Frogs jump
Caterpillars hump

Worms wiggle
Bugs jiggle

Rabbits hop
Horses clop

Snakes slide
Sea gulls glide

Mice creep
Deer leap

Puppies bounce
Kittens pounce

Lions stalk—
But—
I *walk!*

THINGS

William Jay Smith

Trains are for going,
Boats are for rowing,
Seeds are for sowing,
Noses for blowing,
    And sleeping's for bed.

Dogs are for pawing,
Logs are for sawing,
Crows are for cawing,
Rivers for thawing,
    And sleeping's for bed.

Flags are for flying,
Stores are for buying,
Glasses for spying,
Babies for crying,
    And sleeping's for bed.

Cows are for mooing,
Chickens for shooing,
Blue is for bluing,
Things are for doing,
    And sleeping's for bed.

Games are for playing,
Hay is for laying,
Horses for neighing,
Saying's for saying,
    And sleeping's for bed.

·Money's for spending,
Patients for tending,
Branches for bending,
Poems for ending,
    And sleeping's for bed.

BLUM

Dorothy Aldis

Dog means dog,
And cat means cat;
And there are lots
Of words like that.

A cart's a cart
To pull or shove,
A plate's a plate,
To eat off of.

But there are other
Words I say
When I am left
Alone to play.

Blum is one.
Blum is a word
That very few
Have ever heard.

I like to say it,
"Blum, Blum, Blum"—
I do it loud
Or in a hum.

All by itself
It's nice to sing:
It does not mean
A single thing.

THE PICKETY FENCE

David McCord

The pickety fence
The pickety fence
Give it a lick it's
The pickety fence
Give it a lick it's
A clickety fence
Give it a lick it's
A lickety fence
Give it a lick
Give it a lick
Give it a lick
With a rickety stick
Pickety
Pickety
Pickety
Pick

SONG OF THE TRAIN

David McCord

Clickety-clack
Wheels on the track,
This is the way
They begin the attack:
Click-ety-clack,
Click-ety-clack,
Click-ety, *clack*-ety
Click-ety
Clack.

Clickety-clack,
Over the crack,
Faster and faster
The song of the track:
Clickety-clack,
Clickety-clack,
Clickety, clackety
Clackety
Clack.

Riding in front,
Riding in back,
Everyone hears
The song of the track:

Clickety-clack,
Clickety-clack,
Clickety, *clickety*,
Clackety
Clack.

TRAINS

James S. Tippett

Over the mountains,
Over the plains,
Over the rivers,
Here come the trains.

Carrying passengers,
Carrying mail,
Bringing their precious loads
In without fail.

Thousands of freight cars
All rushing on
Through day and darkness,
Through dusk and dawn.

Over the mountains,
Over the plains,
Over the rivers,
Here come the trains.

Rhymes from Mother Goose

If any verse can be said to have universal appeal to young children, it is the nursery rhyme. Nursery rhymes contain elements most enjoyed by children: a variety of rhythms, interesting subject matter, and both partial and complete story lines.

Mother Goose Rhymes are such a good foundation for appreciation of poetry that many wise teachers and parents keep children interested in them as long as possible. Re-reading favorite rhymes and encouraging children to memorize the ones they like the best is a good way to do this.

BANBURY CROSS

Ride a cock-horse to Banbury Cross,
To see a fine lady upon a white horse.
Rings on her fingers, and bells on her toes,
She shall have music wherever she goes.

TO MARKET, TO MARKET

To market, to market to buy a fat pig,
Home again, home again, jiggety jig;
To market, to market, to buy a fat hog,
Home again, home again, jiggety jog;
To market, to market, to buy a plum bun,
Home again, home again, market is done.

LITTLE BOY BLUE

Little boy blue, come blow your horn;
The sheep's in the meadow, the cow's in the
  corn.
Where's the little boy that looks after the
  sheep?
He's under the haystack, fast asleep.

LITTLE JACK HORNER

Little Jack Horner
Sat in a corner
Eating his Christmas pie;
He put in this thumb,
And pulled out a plum,
And said, "What a good boy am I!"

JACK BE NIMBLE

Jack be nimble, Jack be quick,
Jack jump over the candlestick.

JACK SPRAT

Jack Sprat
Could eat no fat,
His wife could eat no lean;
And so,
Between them both,
They licked the platter clean.

JACK AND JILL

Jack and Jill went up the hill,
To fetch a pail of water;
Jack fell down and broke his crown,
And Jill came tumbling after.

Then up Jack got and home did trot
As fast as he could caper;
And went to bed to mend his head
With vinegar and brown paper.

HEY, DIDDLE, DIDDLE

Hey, diddle, diddle!
The cat and the fiddle,
The cow jumped over the moon;
The little dog laughed
To see such sport,
And the dish ran away with the spoon.

HICKORY, DICKORY, DOCK

Hickory, dickory, dock!
The mouse ran up the clock;
The clock struck one, and down he run,
Hickory, dickory, dock!

HICKETY, PICKETY, MY BLACK HEN

Hickety, pickety, my black hen,
She lays eggs for gentlemen;
Gentlemen come every day
To see what my black hen doth lay.
Sometimes nine and sometimes ten,
Hickety, pickety, my black hen.

SEE SAW, MARGERY DAW

See, saw, Margery Daw,
Jenny shall have a new master;
She shall have but a penny a day,
Because she can't work any faster.

TOM, TOM, THE PIPER'S SON

Tom, Tom, the piper's son,
Stole a pig, and away he run,
The pig was eat,
And Tom was beat,
And Tom ran crying down the street.

HUMPTY DUMPTY

Humpty Dumpty sat on a wall,
Humpty Dumpty had a great fall;
All the King's horses,
All the King's men
Couldn't put Humpty together again.

PETER, PETER

Peter, Peter, pumpkin-eater
Had a wife and couldn't keep her;
He put her in a pumpkin shell,
And there he kept her very well.

PETER PIPER

Peter Piper picked a peck of pickled peppers;
A peck of pickled peppers
Peter Piper picked.
If Peter Piper picked a peck of pickled peppers,
Where is the peck of pickled peppers
Peter Piper picked?

LITTLE MISS MUFFET

Little Miss Muffet
Sat on a tuffet,
Eating her curds and whey;
Along came a spider,
And sat down beside her,
And frightened Miss Muffet away.

THERE WAS A LITTLE GIRL

There was a little girl,
And she had a little curl
Right in the middle of her forehead;
When she was good,
She was very, very good,
But when she was bad, she was horrid.

THERE WERE TWO BLACKBIRDS

There were two blackbirds
Sitting on a hill.
The one named Jack,
And the other named Jill.
Fly away Jack!
Fly away Jill;
Come again, Jack!
Come again, Jill!

THERE WAS AN OLD WOMAN

There was an old woman
Lived under a hill;
And if she's not gone,
She lives there still.

THERE WAS AN OLD WOMAN

There was an old woman
  who lived in a shoe.
She had so many children
  she didn't know what to do.
She gave them some broth
  without any bread,
She whipped them all soundly,
  and sent them to bed.

THERE WAS A CROOKED MAN

There was a crooked man,
  and he walked a crooked mile.
He found a crooked sixpence
  upon a crooked stile;
He bought a crooked cat,
  which caught a crooked mouse,
And they all lived together
  in a little crooked house.

BAA, BAA, BLACK SHEEP

Baa, baa, black sheep,
Have you any wool?
Yes sir, yes sir,
Three bags full;
One for the master,
And one for the dame,
And one for the little boy
Who lives in the lane.

PEASE PORRIDGE HOT

Pease porridge hot,
Pease porridge cold,
Pease porridge in the pot
Nine days old.
Some like it hot,
Some like it cold,
Some like it in the pot,
Nine days old.

GEORGIE PORGIE

Georgie Porgie, pudding and pie,
Kissed the girls and made them cry;
When the boys came out to play,
Georgie Porgie ran away.

OLD MOTHER HUBBARD

Old Mother Hubbard,
Went to the cupboard
To get her poor dog a bone;
But when she got there
The cupboard was bare
And so the poor dog had none.

DIDDLE, DIDDLE, DUMPLING

Diddle, diddle, dumpling, my son John
Went to bed with his stockings on;
One shoe off, and one shoe on,
Diddle, diddle, dumpling, my son John

MARY HAD A LITTLE LAMB

Mary had a little lamb,
Its fleece was white as snow;
And everywhere that Mary went
The lamb was sure to go.

It followed her to school one day,
Which was against the rule;
It made the children laugh and play
To see a lamb at school.

And so the teacher turned it out,
But still it lingered near;
And waited patiently about
Till Mary did appear.

Why does the lamb love Mary so?
The eager children cry;
Why, Mary loves the lamb, you know,
The teacher did reply.

ONE, TWO, BUCKLE MY SHOE

One, two, buckle my shoe;
Three, four, shut the door;
Five, six, pick up sticks;
Seven, eight, lay them straight;
Nine, ten, a good fat hen.

ONE, TWO, THREE, FOUR, FIVE

One, two, three, four, five,
I caught a fish alive
Six, seven, eight, nine, ten,
I let him go again.
Why did you let it go?
Because it bit my finger so.
Which finger did it bite?
The little one upon my right.

I DO NOT LIKE THEE, DR. FELL

I do not like thee, Dr. Fell,
The reason why I cannot tell;
But this I know,
And know full well,
I do not like thee, Dr. Fell.

RAIN, RAIN, GO AWAY

Rain, rain, go away;
Come again another day;
Little Johnny wants to play.

LADYBIRD, LADYBIRD

Ladybird, ladybird,
Fly away home!
Your house is on fire,
Your children will burn,
All but one, and her name is Ann,
And she crept under the pudding pan.

LITTLE DROPS OF WATER

Little drops of water,
Little grains of sand
Make the mighty ocean,
And the pleasant land.

HINTS FOR READING POETRY ALOUD

Reading poetry aloud successfully is a three-step process: selection of materials; preparation in advance of reading; reading. Most difficulties of oral reading can be solved in the first two steps. Here are some things to think about as you train yourself to be a better oral reader:

CHOOSING MATERIAL

The poems and verses in this book have been pre-selected for you as examples of poetry which can be read aloud with success. Keep in mind three principles when choosing materials:

1. *The material should appeal to the listeners.* It should be within the present or possible interest span of the children. It should deal with experiences and images that are familiar to children, or worth familiarizing them with. The words should be known or understandable.

2. *The material should appeal to the reader.* You will read more successfully those things that you enjoy. Never read anything you feel is beneath your dignity or beyond your understanding. When you read material that you genuinely like, your reading will be fresher and more interesting to your listeners.

3. *The material should have some inherent value.* Poetry need not have immediate "usefulness," but it should have some good reason for its existence. Worthwhile poetry and verse can be admired for its subject matter, its use of rhythm, or for many other reasons. Choose material which has sharp images, is fresh and original, and is characterized by creative use of language. Any material worth reading aloud should have some value you can identify.

PREPARING MATERIAL IN ADVANCE

To read aloud effectively, you must prepare in advance!

1. *Understand your material.* Don't merely read—think through the meaning, the mood, and the form of the poetry you will read.

2. *Read aloud to yourself.* Your understanding will determine how you read the selection. The next step is to practice reading it aloud to decide the techniques you will employ to communicate your understanding of the selection. Silent reading is never adequate preparation for oral reading. Only reading aloud will let you know which words might trip the tongue, which words or phrases will need special attention and emphasis, what will be the proper speed at which you read, and what will be the proper mood for that selection. This practice is not excessively time consuming, and a few moments of rehearsal can improve oral reading many times over.

3. *Place your material in a convenient location.* Once you have chosen your material, place it in a convenient location—where doesn't matter as long as you can remember where—so that you can find it when you are ready to begin reading. A bookmark, a turned-down page, or even a memorized selection will save you the embarrassment of flipping through pages looking for the appropriate selection.

COMMUNICATING WHILE READING

The main purpose in reading aloud is to communicate effectively. If you are not yet experienced in reading orally, here are some hints that may help you:

1. *Relax.* You will do your best if you can maintain a relaxed, conversational manner.

2. *Don't race.* Reading aloud usually demands a slower pace than natural conversation. Read slowly so that the images can register. A slower pace is particularly important when you read short verse written with great economy of words. Each word must be heard. Sometimes, of course, fast reading is needed for humor or special effect; make sure then that your voice emphasizes certain words and phrases necessary for understanding.

3. *Be responsive to mood.* Match the mood of the material with the tone of your voice and with your manner.

4. *Avoid interruptions.* Train the children to hold questions and comments until the end of the poem. Children should be taught to listen to a whole selection—otherwise you will be plagued with constant interruptions. Never interrupt a verse to explain the meaning of a word. Difficult words or concepts can be explained before or after the reading. Sometimes you might want to explain a word before you read, then ask the children to listen for it as you read. Sometimes you will want to read the poem first, then talk about a word or phrase before re-reading the poem.

5. *Enjoy yourself.* Express by your manner the fact that you yourself enjoy the material. The pleasure of the reader is contagious.

6. *Communicate.* Always remember that your job is to convey the imagery, ideas, and rhythm of the material to the children. You will find that self-consciousness is minimized and natural ability is maximized when you concentrate on your material and the children. Always think of yourself as a communicator.

SUGGESTIONS FOR USING SOME *POEMS AND VERSES TO BEGIN ON*

Following are a few suggestions that may give the teacher ideas on ways to use "poetry-reading time" to good advantage—to inspire creative art activities, teach or reinforce concepts helpful to the children, or use pictures to add meaning to poetry selection, as well as to foster enjoyment.

Pp. 15–16. Children can easily memorize the six short verses on these two pages. Encourage children to memorize those verses that especially please them. Repeat the verse several times until the children are familiar with it. Then you might suggest that they say it with you. "My Mother Said" and "Reflection" seem particularly easy for children to remember. Children like to have favorite verses and memorize them just as they memorize favorite songs.

P. 17. Since "Catherine" is full of visual images, it is a good verse to illustrate with pictures drawn by children. After reading the verse once, you might repeat the reading, taking care to read the first half of the poem slowly, emphasizing with your voice all the things Catherine put into the cake. Have ready crayons and newsprint (as large as is practical) and ask the children to draw what they thought Catherine's cake looked like when she had finished it.

Pp. 18–19. After reading "Feet" you might ask the children to describe or perhaps just list the different things their feet have felt when they have gone barefoot: hot sidewalks, water, mud, weed stubble, bricks. Then ask the children to think of these things and feelings as you read the poem again.

Pp. 22–4. The four verses about baths and tooth-brushing can be read together or separately. They are a welcome addition to classroom discussions about personal hygiene.

P. 25. "Bed in Summer" is based on the fact that in most climates it grows dark earlier in winter than it does in summer; often in summer bedtime comes while it is still light outside. You may have to point this out to children before they can fully appreciate the poem.

Pp. 28–9. Some poems call for more dramatic reading than others. "I Woke Up This Morning" seems to go over more successfully if the reader begins calmly, and gradually lets his voice express greater and greater frustration and exasperation. This approach is indicated in the original edition of the poem by larger and larger type as the poem progresses.

P. 29. Verses like "Toaster Time" must be read in perfect rhythm. Never try to read a verse like this without first practicing it aloud. If necessary, sacrifice enunciation in favor of rhythm, since the rhythm is the basic element of the verse. Sometimes it is helpful to rearrange the lines of a rhythmic poem either on paper or in your mind so they can be more easily read. With "Toaster Time," for instance, think of a four-count rhythm:

1	2	3	4
tick-tick	tick-tick	tick-tick	tick
Toast up	a sandwich	quick-quick	quick
Hamwich	Jamwich	lick-lick	lick!
(rest)	POP!		
(Or rest for	three counts and . . .		POP!)

Pp. 34–5. Too quiet a voice or whispering usually are not wise when reading aloud to children. However, the sugar sound and a watch's "tck-tck" in "Little Sounds" seem to demand a low, quiet voice or actual whispering. Occasional quiet reading sometimes stimulates more attentive listening.

If the children like "Little Sounds," you might ask them to listen to the sounds they hear on their way to school the next day, or better yet, take them for a quiet walk in the halls of the school or briefly outdoors to see how many different sounds they can identify. A directed listening activity can show how many sounds there are around us all the time, if only we will notice them.

P. 36. "Keep a Poem in Your Pocket" makes a nice introduction to the reading of several poems. You can use it again and again to signal "poetry time."

Pp. 42–3. Picture 7 from the Chandler *Paperback Picture Portfolio* is a scene of a city street during a rainstorm. If you have this portfolio, direct the children's attention to the umbrellas, the shining wet streets, and other details of the picture as an introduction to this poem.

Pp. 41–3. As every teacher knows, the weather outside often influences the atmosphere in the classroom. You may want to save these rain poems for rainy days—in fact, you may want to collect a few more to keep in a file in your desk.

Pp. 44–5. If you have the Chandler *Let's See the Animals Portfolio,* you will want to use picture 13 with this verse. It shows a girl being splattered with water at an overactive drinking fountain. You might show the picture first and ask the children what is happening to the girl in the picture. Ask if this has ever happened to any of them. Say that you have a poem about drinking fountains and read the poem.

P. 53. Use picture 1 from the Chandler *Paperback Picture Portfolio* to introduce this poem. Ask the children to determine the boy's mood by asking "What is the boy doing?" and "What do you think he is thinking about?" Allow time for the children's response, then read "The Secret Place."

P. 54. "The Gold-Tinted Dragon" is another poem that is fun for children to illustrate. "Just imagine a dragon any color and any size, pulling you in a wagon. What do you think it would look like? What is a 'dragonly smile'?" Have the children show you how they think the scene would look by drawing it for you.

P. 55. Picture 15 from the Chandler portfolio *Pictures to Read* is a good illustration for "P's The Proud Policeman."

Pp. 56–7. These three poems about traffic signals have been chosen to help reinforce safety concepts that are so important for urban children.

P. 61. "Boo Hoo" is a useful poem for the teacher to memorize, and remember in those troubled moments when young children resort to tears. It can be whispered into the ear of a crying child to distract him from his problems.

Pp. 61–7. Nonsense verse is always fun. Children enjoy the sounds in nonsense verses, and they enjoy the nonsense, the lack of logic.

Pp. 68–9. Picture 34 from the Chandler *Paperback Picture Portfolio* or similar pictures of trains can be used with "Trains" and "Song of the Train."

Pp. 73–86. These nursery rhymes can be repeated again and again in the classroom. Encourage children to memorize as many as they will. When saying the verses together, have the children say them slowly, to bring out the rhythm and rhyme. Make it a habit to encourage the children to repeat the verses slowly, since "Seeing how fast you can say them" usually destroys the natural beauty of the rhymes. When the children have learned the rhymes, chanting them in unison can foster a feeling of "togetherness" in the same way community singing can.

POETRY BOOKS
FOR YOUNGER CHILDREN

Anthologies

Association for Childhood Education International. *Sung Under the Silver Umbrella*. Macmillan. 1962. Carefully selected poems for younger children.

Bissett, Donald J. *Poems And Verses About Animals*. Chandler. 1967. A collection of verses about the animals city children know—zoo animals, park animals, and pets.

Geismer, Barbara P., and Antoinette B. Suter. *Very Young Verses*. Houghton Mifflin. 1945. Very successful collection of poetry about the experiences of young children.

McEwan, Catherine S., ed. *Away We Go!* Thos. Y. Crowell. 1956. Anthology of simple, charming poetry easily shared with children.

Collections of Poetry by Individual Authors

Aldis, Dorothy. *Hello Day*. Putnam. 1959. A reflection of the day-to-day moods of children expressed in common experiences of childhood.

Allen, Marie Louise. *A Pocketful of Poems*. Harper. 1957. Twenty-two light verses in picture book format.

Brown, Margaret Wise. *Nibble, Nibble*. W. R. Scott. 1959. Pleasing poems about insects, the sea, fish, animals, nature. In picture book format, illustrated by Leonard Weisgard.

Chute, Marchette. *Around and About*. Dutton. 1959. Simple verses with obvious rhyme. Many are short and easy to memorize.

De Regniers, Beatrice S. *Something Special*. Harcourt. 1958. Nine verses; imaginative humor and concepts.

Fisher, Aileen. *Going Barefoot*. Thos. Y. Crowell. 1960. A picture book of poetry about a boy's fun and delight in springtime. Illustrated by Adrienne Adams.

Fisher, Aileen. *Runny Days, Sunny Days*. Abelard. 1958.

Light verse on a theme of "Runny days, sunny days, sum-
mertime or fall, blowy days, snowy days—seems I like
them all."

Fisher, Aileen. *Where Does Everyone Go?* Thos. Y. Crowell.
1961. Autumn, and what happens to animals and insects
during fall and winter. Illustrated by Adrienne Adams.

Gay, Zhenya. *Jingle Jangle.* Viking. 1953. Light verses, many
mischievous, profusely illustrated by the author.

Hoberman, Mary Ann. *Hello and Goodby.* Little, Brown. 1959.
Charming verses for the very young.

Kuskin, Karla. *In the Middle of the Trees.* Harper. 1958.
Twenty-one poems in picture book format. Delightful. *The
Rose On My Cake.* Harper. 1964.

Livingston, Myra Cohn. *Whispers. Wide Awake. The Moon
and a Star.* Harcourt. 1958. 1959. 1965. Attractive small
books with light-hearted and thought-provoking verses.

Milne, A. A. *When We Were Very Young. Now We Are Six.*
Dutton. Rev. eds. 1961. A few Britishisms will escape the
children, but Milne is as universal as childhood.

O'Neil, Mary. *Hailstones and Halibut Bones.* Doubleday.
1961. Explores the feeling and the images evoked by
different colors. Illustrated by Leonard Weisgard.

Orleans, Ilo. *I Watch the World Go By.* Walck. 1961. Rhythmic verses illustrated by Pelagie Doane.

Rosetti, Christina. *Sing-Song.* Macmillan. 1924. Rhythmic
verses.

Smith, William Jay. *Laughing Time.* Atlantic-Little, Brown.
1955. A gay book of childlike verses, unusual images.

Spilka, Arnold. *A Lion I Can Do Without.* Walck. 1964. Picture book of poetry illustrated with humorous drawings.

Stevenson, Robert Louis. *A Child's Garden of Verses.* Many
editions, from that with the classic illustrations by Jessie
Willcox Smith (Scribner's, 1905) to the one illustrated
by Tasha Tudor (Walck, 1947). Childlike images and
rhythms.

Tippitt, James. *I Live in a City.* Harper. 1927. Out of print,
but still available in many libraries. Verse about apart-
ments, the park, elevators, etc.

Mother Goose Rhymes

Over a hundred editions of Mother Goose and variants are now in print. A few choice ones are listed below:

Briggs, Raymond. *Mother Goose Treasury.* Coward. 1966. Large, bold, vigorous drawings make this indeed a treasure chest of Mother Goose.

Brooke, Leslie. *Ring O'Roses.* Warne, n.d. A few popular rhymes with detailed illustrations which children study with fascination.

De Angeli, Marguerite. *Marguerite de Angeli's Book of Nursery and Mother Goose Rhymes.* Doubleday. 1954. An unusually large collection with beautiful drawings.

Lines, Katherine. *Lavender's Blue.* Watts. 1954. Illustrations by Harold Jones. A collection of rhymes that bears the stamp of originality.

Smith, Jessie Willcox. *The Little Mother Goose.* Dodd, Mead, n.d. Only a few color illustrations, but girls like its handy size.

Tudor, Tasha. *Mother Goose.* Walck. 1944. A delicate edition, just right for dainty little girls.

Wildsmith, Brian. *Brian Wildsmith's Mother Goose.* Watts. 1964. A well-rounded collection of some familiar, some less familiar rhymes. The artist's brilliant colors give the book a happy tone.

Wright, Blanche Fisher. *The Real Mother Goose.* Rand McNally. 1916. Clear, brightly colored drawings. Often the favorite of children who are exposed to many editions of Mother Goose.

INDEX OF TITLES

INDEX OF FIRST LINES